Number Problems

1 Complete these number sequences.

a 109 → 118 → [ ] → 136 → [ ] → [ ] → 163 → [ ]

b [ ] → [ ] → 392 → [ ] → [ ] → [ ] → 452 → 467

c 215 → [ ] → [ ] → 278 → 299 → [ ] → [ ] → [ ]

d [ ] → –16 → –9 → [ ] → [ ] → [ ] → 19 → [ ]

2 Draw a triangle around the triangular numbers.

11   45   38   15   21   16   47   36   29

3 Write down any other triangular numbers less than 50.

[ ]

4 Write these amounts in words.

a 4090

b 3800

c 37 003

d 506 040

5 Write these amounts in figures.

a three thousand and eight [ ]

b thirty thousand, four hundred and nine [ ]

c six hundred and nine thousand, two hundred and five [ ]

Number Problems

1 How many...

a	hundreds in 4695?	
b	tens in 83 720?	
c	thousands in 521 698?	

d	tens in 69 005?	
e	hundreds in 384 711?	
f	thousands in 1 039 704?	

2 Join each number to its correct box.

20 001   10 468 135   2014   200 659   4 846 392

less than twenty thousand	more than one million but less than ten million	between twenty thousand and two hundred thousand

between two hundred thousand and one million	more than ten million

3 Read these problems and work out the answers.

a Add eight hundred and twenty-six to the product of 1425 and five.

b Calculate one twelfth of 1080 and multiply your result by nine.

c What number is three hundred and fifty more than 64 + 37?

d Share a half of 2380 by ten and then treble the answer.

4 Draw a square around the square numbers.

25   33   16   96   49   28   81   74

5 Write down any other square numbers up to 144.

Number Problems

1 Shade number 1 on the grid and all multiples of 2, 3, 5 and 7 except 2, 3, 5 and 7 themselves.

1	2	3	4	5	6	7	8	9	10	11	12	13	14	15	16	17	18	19	20
21	22	23	24	25	26	27	28	29	30	31	32	33	34	35	36	37	38	39	40
41	42	43	44	45	46	47	48	49	50	51	52	53	54	55	56	57	58	59	60
61	62	63	64	65	66	67	68	69	70	71	72	73	74	75	76	77	78	79	80
81	82	83	84	85	86	87	88	89	90	91	92	93	94	95	96	97	98	99	100

Write out the unshaded numbers and say what they are called.

2 Cross out the incorrect word in the brackets. If in doubt, test each statement yourself.

a The product of two even numbers is (odd, even).

b The product of two odd numbers is (odd, even).

c The product of one odd number and one even number is (odd, even).

3 Break down each number in the same way as the one done for you.

a 4957 = $4000 + 900 + 50 + 7$ **c** 85 603 =

b 6321 =   **d** 72 984 =

4 Complete this number sequence.

360 → 341 → ☐ → ☐ → ☐ → 265 → ☐ → ☐

5 Solve this problem.

| 17 | | ×6 | | +98 | | ÷25 | | ×301 | | −21 | | +113 | = | |

3

Place Value & Ordering

1 Fill in the missing numbers in the table below.

Number in words	M	HTh	TTh	Th	H	T	U
a three hundred and six							
b five thousand and eighty-nine							
c four hundred and five thousand and twenty-six							
d two million, eighty thousand, three hundred and seventy							
e thirty thousand, two hundred and one							

2 Arrange these numbers in ascending order from left to right.

123 645   124 653   123 465   124 365   123 456

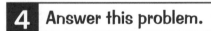

3 Arrange these numbers in descending order from left to right.

780 945   784 950   795 048   789 504

4 Answer this problem.

Write down the digit in the hundredths place in this number: 48.253

5 Write a number in each empty box so that the four numbers in each column are in orde

a	25 870	**b**		**c**		**d**		**e**	
			55 109		10 000		60 606		98 889
	25 875				9990				99 999
			56 109				56 109		

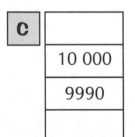

4

Place Value & Ordering

1 Write as a numeral the value of the **5** in each of these numbers.

a

17 583	8.265	576 928	305.08	5 431 620

b

357 093	36.05	4856.91	85 406	694.572

2 Write the whole numbers shown in Question 1 in words.
Start with the largest and put them in descending order.

3 Place the signs > < or = between each pair to make the statement correct.

a 3 hundreds ☐ 30 tens

b 6 thousands ☐ 50 hundreds

c 40 thousands ☐ 5 thousands

d 500 hundreds ☐ 5100 tens

e 700 thousands ☐ 7000 hundreds

f 9000 hundreds ☐ 80 000 tens

4 Make the biggest integer you can with each set of digits.

a 3, 7, 5, 8, 4, 0, 6, 1 ☐

b 9, 2, 5, 5, 4, 7, 4, 8 ☐

5 Make the smallest integer you can with each set of digits. Use all the digits.

a 6, 3, 9, 7, 5, 4, 4, 3 ☐

b 9, 2, 6, 2, 9, 8, 6, 6 ☐

Place Value & Ordering

1. Write the correct number in each box.

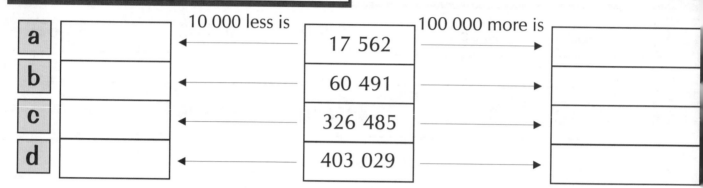

a		10 000 less is ←	17 562	→ 100 000 more is	
b		←	60 491	→	
c		←	326 485	→	
d		←	403 029	→	

2. What number is half way between:

a	25 300 and 26 500?	
b	40 500 and 20 100?	
c	26 750 and 27 250?	

d	325 900 and 325 970?	
e	484 850 and 485 950?	
f	630 000 and 590 500?	

3. Arrange these numbers in order in the boxes.

103   −104   −99   106   98   −101   100   −107

Lowest [ ] [ ] [ ] [ ] [ ] [ ] [ ] [ ] Highest

4. Put these fractional and decimal amounts in order of size starting with the largest.

0.5 $\frac{5}{6}$ $\frac{1}{12}$ 0.25 $\frac{4}{10}$ 0.75 $\frac{3}{5}$ 0.99 $\frac{1}{6}$ $\frac{1}{3}$ 0.2

[ ] [ ] [ ] [ ] [ ] [ ] [ ] [ ] [ ] [ ] [ ]

5. Answer these problems.

a | In the decimal 4.805 give the digit in the thousandths place. | [ ]

b | Total these amounts and give your answer in decimal form: $3 + \frac{6}{10} + \frac{9}{1000} + \frac{4}{100}$ | [ ]

Estimating

1 Would you estimate these quantities to the nearest 10, 100, 1000, 10 000, 100 000 or 1 000 000?

a	the size of a theatre audience
b	the number of trees in the world
c	the number of books on a mobile library van
d	the number of chairs in a school classroom

2 Join each number in Circle A to a number in Circle B that is approximately half its size.

A
35 321
7510
4958
49 612
42 106
31 658

B
3700
2500
24 000
18 200
15 600
21 000

Which 2 numbers in Circle A add up to roughly 12 500?

3 Round these decimal amounts to the nearest whole number.

a 26.49   **b** 148.02   **c** 199.51   **d** 100.5

4 Round these decimal numbers to the nearest tenth.

a 35.84   **b** 174.36   **c** 461.59   **d** 95.23

5 Circle the best approximation in the box for each calculation.

a	60.9 – 59.8	6.09 – 59.8	609 – 598	61 – 60	60 – 59
b	38.2 + 53.1	382 + 531	39 + 54	3.82 + 5.31	38 + 53

Estimating

1 Round these numbers to the nearest 100.

a 24 301 [ ] **b** 36 875 [ ] **c** 72 050 [ ]

2 Write the answer to each calculation in the first box. Then write in the second box the amount from the list below that is closest to the actual answer.

| 7600 | 4 | 0.08 | 23 | 5800 | $\frac{1}{2}$ |

a 3900 ÷ 1000 = [ ] [ ] **d** 9524 − 3759 = [ ] [ ]

b 0.9 × 25 = [ ] [ ] **e** 75 ÷ 1000 = [ ] [ ]

c 4275 + 3306 = [ ] [ ] **f** 0.005 + 0.5 = [ ] [ ]

3 Write a number to the nearest whole 50 that is roughly a quarter of each of these numbers.

a 1989 [ ] **c** 9210 [ ] **e** 8995 [ ]

b 3001 [ ] **d** 5599 [ ] **f** 4803 [ ]

4 On the number lines estimate the numbers marked by the arrows.

a
20 000 [ ] [ ] [ ] 30 000

b
− 50 [ ] [ ] [ ] [ ] 50

5 Round these fractional amounts to the nearest whole number.

a $56\frac{2}{3}$ [ ] **b** $78\frac{5}{12}$ [ ] **c** $91\frac{2}{5}$ [ ] **d** $25\frac{4}{7}$ [ ] **e** $64\frac{1}{2}$ [ ]

Estimating

1 Round these numbers to the nearest 1000.

a 603 504 [ ]   **c** 185 999 [ ]   **e** 427 465 [ ]

b 396 405 [ ]   **d** 518 500 [ ]   **f** 274 499 [ ]

2 Circle the two values that are roughly the same in each row.

a 0.04 $\frac{3}{100}$ 33% $\frac{6}{10}$ **d** $\frac{3}{4}$ 3.04   74%   7.34

b $\frac{7}{100}$ 71%   0.17 $\frac{7}{10}$ **e** 8.3 $\frac{7}{16}$ 10% $\frac{3}{8}$

c 3.9 $\frac{3}{9}$ 33% $\frac{3}{12}$ **f** $\frac{1}{2}$ 94%   2.1   0.49

3 On the number lines estimate the decimal numbers marked by the arrows.

a

0 [ ] [ ] [ ] [ ] 1

b

0 [ ] [ ] [ ] [ ] 0.1

4 Write a number to the nearest 100 that is approximately a tenth of each of these numbers.

a 10 007 [ ]   **c** 30 128 [ ]   **e** 44 739 [ ]

b 24 877 [ ]   **d** 14 992 [ ]   **f** 19 985 [ ]

5 Circle the number that is closest to the number in the box.

a [35 000]   34 251   35 750   **c** [80 000]   94 250   66 750

b [15 250]   16 825   13 758   **d** [55 000]   54 215   55 780

Fractions, Decimals & Percentages

---

1 On this strip, colour 0.5 red and 0.05 green.

---

2 Write these mixed numbers as improper fractions.

a $6\frac{1}{3}$ ☐   **c** $5\frac{5}{6}$ ☐   **e** $8\frac{1}{4}$ ☐   **g** $9\frac{5}{8}$ ☐

b $7\frac{1}{8}$ ☐   **d** $9\frac{7}{12}$ ☐   **f** $8\frac{5}{12}$ ☐   **h** $4\frac{5}{12}$ ☐

---

3 Find the answers to these problems.

a A robot can make $2\frac{1}{2}$ cars in an hour.
How many cars can it make in 36 hours? ☐

b Look at the decimal, 594.372. Give the correct digit for each place value.

1) thousandths ☐   2) ones ☐   3) hundredths ☐   4) tenths ☐

c A beetle travels 1 metre in $1\frac{1}{2}$ minutes.
How long will it take to travel 40 metres? ☐

---

4 Work out 10% of these amounts.

a 160 ☐   **c** 370 ☐   **e** 110 ☐   **g** 50 ☐   **i** 120 ☐

b 640 ☐   **d** 800 ☐   **f** 450 ☐   **h** 780 ☐   **j** 290 ☐

---

5 Do each question in the same way as the one done for you.

a 45.86 = $40 + 5 + \frac{8}{10} + \frac{6}{100}$ **d** 0.045 = ☐

b 680.1 = ☐   **e** 6.325 = ☐

c 52.036 = ☐   **f** 0.846 = ☐

Fractions, Decimals & Percentages

1 Do these fraction additions. Give each answer in its lowest terms.

a $\frac{8}{12} + \frac{1}{4}$ ☐   **c** $\frac{1}{3} + \frac{1}{12}$ ☐   **e** $\frac{5}{8} + \frac{1}{4}$ ☐   **g** $\frac{3}{8} + \frac{1}{2}$ ☐

b $\frac{6}{12} + \frac{1}{6}$ ☐   **d** $\frac{1}{2} + \frac{1}{8}$ ☐   **f** $\frac{1}{2} + \frac{3}{4}$ ☐   **h** $\frac{1}{4} + \frac{7}{12}$ ☐

2 On this strip, colour 0.2 blue and 0.25 yellow.

3 Change these improper fractions into mixed numbers.

a $\frac{59}{9}$ ☐   **c** $\frac{38}{7}$ ☐   **e** $\frac{19}{5}$ ☐   **g** $\frac{45}{2}$ ☐   **i** $\frac{25}{7}$ ☐

b $\frac{28}{5}$ ☐   **d** $\frac{29}{8}$ ☐   **f** $\frac{31}{3}$ ☐   **h** $\frac{53}{10}$ ☐   **j** $\frac{42}{5}$ ☐

4 Fill in the empty spaces on the chart. The first one is done to get you started.

	Decimal number	Expanded Form (decimals)	Mixed Number	Expanded Form (fractions)
a	3.47	3 + 0.4 + 0.07	$3\frac{47}{100}$	$3 + \frac{4}{10} + \frac{7}{100}$
b	15.93			
c	21.607			

5 Work out 20% of these amounts.

a 400 ☐   **c** 350 ☐   **e** 140 ☐   **g** 170 ☐   **i** 450 ☐

b 300 ☐   **d** 900 ☐   **f** 210 ☐   **h** 215 ☐   **j** 530 ☐

Fractions, Decimals & Percentages

1   Work out these decimal addition and subtraction problems.

a	5.48 + 97.69		**d**	91.95 – 14.1		**g**	7.73 + 271.8	
b	67.2 – 56.98		**e**	0.87 + 3.046		**h**	97.86 – 3.4	
c	1.964 + 0.3		**f**	8 – 1.037		**i**	86.43 + 0.42	

2   Change these percentages into fractions in their lowest terms.

a	80%		**c**	55%		**e**	10%		**g**	95%		**i**	50%	
b	40%		**d**	75%		**f**	15%		**h**	25%		**j**	30%	

3   Do these subtraction calculations. Give each answer in its lowest terms.

a	$\frac{3}{4} - \frac{3}{12}$		**c**	$\frac{1}{2} - \frac{5}{12}$		**e**	$\frac{1}{4} - \frac{1}{12}$		**g**	$\frac{1}{4} - \frac{1}{8}$	
b	$\frac{2}{8} - \frac{2}{12}$		**d**	$\frac{1}{4} - \frac{1}{6}$		**f**	$\frac{1}{2} - \frac{1}{12}$		**h**	$\frac{2}{3} - \frac{3}{6}$	

4   Find the following amounts.

a	$\frac{7}{12}$ of 5316		**e**	$\frac{8}{9}$ of 8802		**i**	$\frac{5}{8}$ of 6440	
b	$\frac{3}{8}$ of 8040		**f**	$\frac{2}{7}$ of 3227		**j**	$\frac{2}{9}$ of 5616	
c	$\frac{4}{9}$ of 3276		**g**	$\frac{1}{6}$ of 4356		**k**	$\frac{6}{7}$ of 5313	
d	$\frac{7}{10}$ of 5700		**h**	$\frac{5}{9}$ of 9378		**l**	$\frac{1}{8}$ of 6832	

5   Convert the following percentages into decimals.

a	25%		**c**	7%		**e**	37%		**g**	75%		**i**	30%	
b	15%		**d**	40%		**f**	1%		**h**	65%		**j**	43%	

Adding

1 Using multiples of 5 or 10 write two 2-digit numbers that add up to the amounts given below.

a	115	+	d	185	+	g	130	+
b	145	+	e	160	+	h	150	+
c	180	+	f	155	+	i	175	+

2 Solve these problems.

a Add 916 and 921 to 694 and nine hundred and fifty-five.

b What amount results from adding 586, 520, 827 and six hundred and thirty-eight?

c Combine two thousand and eighty-seven, 6059 and 1099.

d What number is two hundred and sixty-nine more than 567 plus 598?

3 Connect each calculation to its answer.

6425 + 2565	4479 + 2145	3163 + 3979	1279 + 5275	3218 + 3319

6624	6537	8990	7142	6554

4 Use any suitable method to add **4300** to each of these numbers in your head.

a	6250		b	8540		c	7990	

5 Double each of these numbers.

a	21 804		d	18 513		g	15 692	
b	19 365		e	22 746		h	14 284	
c	24 076		f	17 539		i	28 075	

Adding

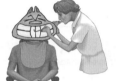

---

1 Work out in your head the missing amounts in these sums.

a 205 + 775 = [ ]   **d** 570 + 840 = [ ]   **g** 535 + 475 = [ ]

b [ ] + 740 = 1480   **e** [ ] + 5900 = 13 100   **h** [ ] + 870 = 1740

c 45 + [ ] = 1000   **f** 825 + [ ] = 1390   **i** 430 + [ ] = 1100

---

2 Fill in the missing numbers in these charts.

a

+	1725	1575
1450		3025
1650		
1850	3575	

b

+	1375	1525
1290	2665	
1470		
1630		3155

---

3 How many steps of 1250 are there from:

a 2500 to 8750? [ ]   **b** 6250 to 0? [ ]   **c** 10 000 to 1250? [ ]

0   2500   5000   7500   10 000

---

4 Look at these addition squares and then fill them in. The first one has been done for you.

a

950	1250	2200
1140	6250	7390
2090	7500	9590

b

	625	2670
745		4110
	3990	

c

680	4095	
	425	1205
1460		

---

5 Add together each pair of numbers.

a 4692, 2033 [ ]   **b** 3359, 3472 [ ]   **c** 5978, 2454 [ ]

Adding

1 Work out the answers to these column additions.

| a | 4604 +3336 | b | 4578 +5368 | c | 2454 +5978 | d | 4465 +4965 | e | 9763 +5687 |

a | 4604
  | +3336
  | _____

b | 4578
  | +5368
  | _____

c | 2454
  | +5978
  | _____

d | 4465
  | +4965
  | _____

e | 9763
  | +5687
  | _____

2 Double the first amount and then double the answer. The first one is done for you.

a	1040	2080	4160	d	1580			g	2270		
b	1630			e	2150			h	1280		
c	2470			f	1390			i	2160		

3 Use all these numbers to make ten addition calculations. Have three numbers in each sum.

☐ + ☐ + ☐ = ☐

☐ + ☐ + ☐ = ☐

☐ + ☐ + ☐ = ☐

☐ + ☐ + ☐ = ☐

☐ + ☐ + ☐ = ☐

195	184	260	218	287
316	247	125	192	333
176	168	326	259	151
282	332	251	319	240
327	319	331	263	179
103	135	278	320	314

☐ + ☐ + ☐ = ☐

☐ + ☐ + ☐ = ☐

☐ + ☐ + ☐ = ☐

☐ + ☐ + ☐ = ☐

☐ + ☐ + ☐ = ☐

4 Solve each problem and write your answer in words.

a Make 1165 greater by 1766.

b Find the total of 2378, 2156 and 2439.

5 Here's a challenge to your addition skills.

a 8795 + 48 + 233 + 6 = ☐   b 950 + 7 + 4289 + 63 = ☐

Subtracting

---

1 By any suitable method, subtract **820** from each of these numbers in your head.

a 8000 [ ]   **b** 6700 [ ]   **c** 4010 [ ]

---

2 Connect each calculation to its answer.

| 7090 – 1258 | 9256 – 3809 | 8600 – 3213 | 7535 – 1177 | 7625 – 1938 |

| 6358 | 5832 | 5447 | 5687 | 5387 |

---

3 Subtract any 2-digit number from any 3-digit number to give the answer shown.

a [ ] – [ ] = 56   **d** [ ] – [ ] = 763   **g** [ ] – [ ] = 957

b [ ] – [ ] = 125   **e** [ ] – [ ] = 398   **h** [ ] – [ ] = 501

c [ ] – [ ] = 642   **f** [ ] – [ ] = 480   **i** [ ] – [ ] = 850

---

4 In the right-hand box write a subtraction fact using all three numbers from the left-hand box.

a 340, 998, 658 | *998 – 658 = 340*   **d** 226, 407, 181 |

b 854, 238, 616 | **e** 940, 817, 123 |

c 213, 423, 210 | **f** 319, 700, 381 |

---

5 Solve these problems.

a Subtract 129 from four hundred and sixty-seven. [ ]

b Eight hundred and seventy-six minus three hundred and ninety-nine. [ ]

c 287 less than 900 is how many? [ ]

d How many more than five thousand, three hundred and ninety-five is 6709? [ ]

Subtracting

1 Each number in a box should have a multiple of a hundred and one other number connected to it to make a correct subtraction sum.

487   600   195   400   311   338   700   900   175   500

362	289	413	225	305

2 Work out in your head the missing amounts in these subtraction facts.

a $1200 - 325 =$ ⬚

b ⬚ $- 475 = 535$

c $1350 -$ ⬚ $= 800$

d $1400 - 650 =$ ⬚

e ⬚ $- 725 = 525$

f $1500 -$ ⬚ $= 625$

g $1300 - 975 =$ ⬚

h ⬚ $- 750 = 700$

i $1020 -$ ⬚ $= 595$

3 Solve these problems.

a How many more than seven hundred and thirty-eight is 3958? ⬚

b Find the difference between 7514 and 3965. ⬚

4 Fill in the missing numbers in these charts.

a

–	2100	3001
1263		1738
1945		
1781	319	

b

–	15 750	18 376
3876	11 874	
5345		
8013		10 363

5 Subtract the smallest number from the largest number.

a 5635, 1058 ⬚   **b** 3872, 6254 ⬚   **c** 9285, 4689 ⬚

Subtracting

1 **Work out the answers to these column subtractions.**

a	5070	**b**	8734	**c**	7000	**d**	8259	**e**	9353
	− 4801		− 3170		− 4728		− 5780		− 4388

2 Complete each of these subtraction problems by choosing any number from the grid once.

512 − 159 − ☐ = ☐

873 − ☐ − 292 = ☐

641 − 264 − ☐ = ☐

978 − ☐ − 146 = ☐

792 − 176 − ☐ = ☐

158	133
106	187
122	161
194	145
175	190

756 − ☐ − 239 = ☐

590 − 128 − ☐ = ☐

652 − 187 − 113 = 352

934 − 285 − ☐ = ☐

886 − ☐ − 207 = ☐

3 How many do you need to subtract from each number to leave fifteen hundred?
Try to work out the answers mentally before checking with pencil and paper methods.

a	2856		**c**	6194		**e**	9407		**g**	7283	
b	4930		**d**	8626		**f**	5375		**h**	3518	

4 Solve each problem and write your answer in words.

a From 8762 subtract 5247. ☐

b How many more than 405 is 3225? ☐

5 Here's a challenge to your subtraction skills.

a 7206 − 27 − 259 − 9 = ☐   **b** 13 243 − 376 − 8 − 66 = ☐

18

Multiplying

1 Write the square of these numbers.

a 9		**d** 12		**g** 50		**j** 70	
b 40		**e** 10		**h** 30		**k** 90	
c 20		**f** 60		**i** 80		**l** 100	

2 Make these numbers fifteen times larger without using pencil and paper.

a 12   **b** 14   **c** 18   **d** 25   **e** 33

3 Treble each number and write your answer in words.

a 27 490

b 18 651

c 32 008

4 Draw a line to connect each calculation to its answer.

7 × 657	701 × 6	5 × 890	591 × 8	523 × 9

4206	4450	4599	4707	4728

5 Solve these problems:

a Three hundred and thirty-two multiplied by six.

b One hundred and eighty is a fifth of what number?

c Make the number that is four times the size of 297 ten times bigger.

d Multiply the product of one hundred and twenty-eight and 9 by seven.

Multiplying

1 Circle the numbers that are multiples of 9.

499   90   168   1440   468   1504   423   1080

189   1322   1170   427   540   1530   575   378

2 Work out the missing numbers in your head.

a $30 \times 6 = \boxed{}$

b $\boxed{} \times 5 = 75$

c $8 \times \boxed{} = 480$

d $25 \times 5 = \boxed{}$

e $\boxed{} \times 7 = 350$

f $8 \times \boxed{} = 640$

g $9 \times 70 = \boxed{}$

h $\boxed{} \times 6 = 240$

i $7 \times \boxed{} = 630$

3 Multiply each number by eight and write the answer in the lower box.

a 1573	**b** 6492	**c** 3210	**d** 8958	**e** 5386

4 Write the product of each pair of numbers.

a 362, 37 $\boxed{}$

b 18, 389 $\boxed{}$

c 594, 25 $\boxed{}$

d 22, 424 $\boxed{}$

e 481, 49 $\boxed{}$

f 34, 207 $\boxed{}$

5 Fill in the missing numbers in these charts.

a

×	275	550
4	1100	
8		
16		8800

b

×	225	450
6		2700
12		
24	5400	

20

Multiplying

1 Work out the answers to these multiplications.

a	8 1 6 4	b	5 3 8 6	c	3 6 8 2	d	6 9 3 5	e	8 2 6 8
	× 4		× 8		× 6		× 9		× 7

2 Solve these problems.

a   Treble the value of 5574 and multiply the answer by ten.

b   If a ninth of a number is 1543, what is the number?

c   Eleven groups of eight hundred and sixty-three gives a total of how many?

d   Change nine hundred and seven into a number five times the size.

3 Write six numbers which are multiples of eight and greater than 200.

a

Now write six numbers which are multiples of 4 and 6 and greater than 100.

b

4 Circle and join each number in the top row to a number 20 times its size in the bottom row.

(102)	137	146	120	109	115	154	128	143
2860	(2040)	2740	2560	3080	2400	2300	2920	2180

5 Write down the answers to these tricky multiplications.

a   345 × 7 × 8 × 9 =

b   270 × 6 × 7 × 8 =

Dividing

---

1 — Use appropriate mental methods to make these numbers nine times smaller.

a 459 ☐   **c** 657 ☐   **e** 936 ☐   **g** 486 ☐   **i** 171 ☐

b 585 ☐   **d** 270 ☐   **f** 981 ☐   **h** 729 ☐   **j** 954 ☐

2 — Find one–seventh of each of these numbers and write your answer in words.

a 4557 ☐

b 8099 ☐

c 9730 ☐

d 7196 ☐

3 — Connect each calculation to its answer.

| $5125 \div 5$ | $9486 \div 9$ | $6468 \div 6$ | $8520 \div 8$ | $7854 \div 7$ |

(1078)   (1065)   (1054)   (1025)   (1122)

4 — Solve these problems.

a Calculate a quarter of seven hundred and sixty-eight and then halve your answer. ☐

b Find a third of six thousand, two hundred and fifty-two. ☐

c Write two numbers with a quotient of 15. ☐

5 — Write each answer in the box, including the number left over.

a $548 \div 3$ ☐ r ☐   **b** $842 \div 6$ ☐ r ☐   **c** $842 \div 9$ ☐ r ☐

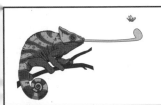

Dividing

1 Work out the missing amounts in your head.

a 450 ÷ 9 = ☐   **d** 720 ÷ 9 = ☐   **g** 480 ÷ 8 = ☐

b ☐ ÷ 5 = 100   **e** ☐ ÷ 7 = 70   **h** ☐ ÷ 8 = 80

c 630 ÷ ☐ = 90   **f** 120 ÷ ☐ = 20   **i** 420 ÷ ☐ = 7

2 Divide each number by eight and write the answer in the lower box.

a	8240	b	8352	c	2696	d	3264	e	9576
	☐		☐		☐		☐		☐

3 Fill in the missing numbers in these two charts.

a

÷	2800	12480
20	140	
40		
80		156

b

÷	59 280	23 880
30		796
60		
120	494	

4 For each of these numbers, write down as many pairs of factors as you can.

a 144

b 168

c 180

5 Solve each problem and write your answer in words.

a Share 225 between 15.

b What is the remainder when 3417 is divided by 20?

23

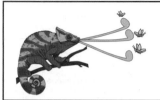

Dividing

---

1 Work out the answers to these division calculations. Some have remainders.

a 2 | 1 6 5 4

c 6 | 4 7 8 2

e 5 | 6 7 0 1

g 8 | 5 3 1 2

b 4 | 3 6 9 2

d 3 | 2 1 3 1

f 9 | 1 8 5 7

h 7 | 7 2 6 8

---

2 In the right-hand box, write a division fact using all three numbers from the left-hand box.

a	772, 4, 193	772 ÷ 4 = 193	**d**	7, 595, 85	
b	5, 305, 61		**e**	97, 776, 8	
c	146, 6, 876		**f**	171, 9, 19	

---

3 Solve these problems.

a 3810 contains how many sets of six?

b Find a ninth of 936 and then work out a quarter of the answer.

---

4 Circle the calculation that has the same answer as the large number.

a **625** | 5000 ÷ 8 / 6000 ÷ 10

c **183** | 1448 ÷ 8 / 1281 ÷ 7

e **1007** | 8099 ÷ 7 / 9063 ÷ 9

b **408** | 7185 ÷ 5 / 2856 ÷ 7

d **271** | 2439 ÷ 9 / 3060 ÷ 10

f **700** | 7056 ÷ 9 / 6300 ÷ 9

---

5 Write down the answers to these chewy divisions.

a 127 008 ÷ 6 ÷ 7 ÷ 8 =

b 8940 ÷ 3 ÷ 4 ÷ 5 =

24

Money Problems

1 Solve these problems. Write the answers in the answer boxes below the questions.

a Find the difference in cost between seven pizzas at £2.36 each and five lasagnes at £2.25 each.

b Colin has £8.30. Helen has three fifths of this amount. How much have they altogether?

c Tara has spent $\frac{1}{6}$ of her pocket money on a book and $\frac{2}{3}$ of her money on some jeans. What fraction of her money was unspent?

d 11 children each had an equal share of a sum of money. They each received £1.18 and there was 2p left over. Find the sum of money.

e Work out the change you'd get from £16.00 after spending £9.48 and £5.82.

a	b	c	d	e

2 Work out the original cost for each half-price amount shown below.

a £27.16 [ ]   **b** £49.20 [ ]   **c** £35.13 [ ]

3 How much does one of each cost?

a 10 for £4.60 [ ]   **b** 9 for £14.04 [ ]   **c** 5 for £11.00 [ ]

4 Subtract each of these amounts from £100. Give your answer using the £ sign.

a 97p [ ]   **b** 1434p [ ]   **c** £81.29 [ ]

5 Work out the answers to these questions in your head.

a 25 FIFTIES + 25 TENS = [ ]   **c** £4.89 – £2.22 – 42p = [ ]

b (£4.75 + £2.25) ÷ 14 = [ ]   **d** £0.14 × 15 × 2 = [ ]

Money Problems

1 Siobhan had £12.60 which she spent in the way shown on the diagram.

BOOKS	PENS	PAPER

a How much did Siobhan spend on books?

b How much did she spend on pens and paper?

c How much more did Siobhan spend on pens than paper?

2 Write your answers using the £ sign on this addition chart.

+	135p	467p	692p	813p	246p	581p	759p	324p	978p
£5.99		£10.66						£9.23	

3 Give the answers in pence for this subtraction chart.

−	£4.52	£9.05	£5.09	£1.30	£3.24	£6.77	£2.16	£7.51	£8.43
£11.27			618p				911p		

4 Solve these problems.

a One third of Sally's money amounts to £14.38. How much is all her money worth?

b Peter has £8.47 and spends $\frac{3}{7}$ of it on a football. What did the football cost?

c Work out the cost of 928 pencils if they sell at £1.20 for eight.

5 Divide these answers by six and then give your answer as a percentage of 50p.

a	£1.74	29p	58%		**c**	£2.10				**e**	£2.46		
b	£1.02				**d**	£1.44				**f**	£2.58		

Money Problems

1 Use this department store sale sign to help work out the price reduction on each of these items.

SUPER SALE
All items reduced by
12p in the £.

a camera
£34.50 [   ]

b scientific calculator
£9.75 [   ]

c mobile phone
£47.25 [   ]

d minidisc player
£115.50 [   ]

What percentage is the reduction on all of these items? [   ] %

2 Double the value shown and then treble that answer.

a

£20.79	£41.58	£124.74
£35.15		
£16.31		

b

£51.02		
£48.47		
£67.64		

c

£94.53		
£72.80		
£83.26		

3 Keep dividing by 5 until you reach the last amount in each row.

a	£459 375.00	£91 875.00	£18 375.00	£3675.00	£735.00	£147.00
b	£39 062.50					£12.50
c	£4312.50					£1.38

4 Solve this problem. Write your answer both numerically and in words.

£7.32 + £5.23 + £2.05 = [   ] [   ]

5 Work out this problem in your head. Then check it using pencil and paper methods.

A DVD is bought for £17.46 and sold for £26.82. How much profit was made on the deal?

[   ]

Money Problems

1 **Work out this problem in your head. Then check it using pencil and paper methods.**

How many tapes in packs of five for £2.50 can be purchased for £32.40?

2 **Solve this problem. Write your answer both numerically and in words.**

£2.04 + 85p + £0.91 + 78p =

3 **Look at the price list below and then answer the questions.**

Box file	£7.36	Printer toner	£9.99	Mouse mat	£0.94
Document wallet	£0.91	Fax roll	£3.24	Jotter pad	£0.49
A4 ringbinder	£0.75	Pocket calculator	£1.95	Lever arch file	£8.36
Clipboard	£1.10	Desk diary	£3.86	Plastic folder	£1.89

a What is the total cost of 2 box files, a pocket calculator, a fax roll and 3 plastic folders?

b Work out the difference in price between the most expensive and least expensive item.

c Which item is £2.92 more than the mouse mat?

d How much would a 10% discount on the clipboard, jotter pad, A4 ringbinder, document wallet and pocket calculator reduce their total cost?

What is their new total cost?

e How many of the cheapest item could you buy if you had enough money to buy the most expensive? How much money would you have left over?

4 **Work out this multistep problem.**

Find the total cost of 12kg of carrots at £0.42 per ½kg and 9kg of sprouts at 16p per ¼kg.

5 **Express the answer to this problem in words.**

(60% of £8.00) – (40% of 600p) =

Measuring Problems

1 Work out the area of rectangles A-D in mm² and write each answer in the appropriate box.

A

B   B =

D =

D

A =

C   C =

2 Find the total area for all four rectangles in Question 1, multiply it by **4**, divide it by **8** and record your final answer in cm².

Record in cm the total perimeter of all four shapes shown in the first question.

3 Solve these problems.

a The sides of a cube each measure 8 cm.
Find the total surface area in cm² for two cubes of this size.

b A rectangular paddock 180 metres wide needed 956 metres of fencing to enclose it.

What length is the paddock?

c A school hall is $1\frac{1}{6}$ times as long as it is wide. Its width is 18m.

What is its area in m²?

4 Add these millimetre amounts and write your answer in centimetres.

a 102, 113, 95

c 267, 345, 218

e 227, 58, 135

b 235, 184, 321

d 173, 396, 81

f 149, 280, 141

5 How many metres in the following distances?

a 4.5km

b 15.25km

c 27.025km

Measuring Problems

---

1 How many grams in the following kilogram amounts?

a 3.207kg [   ]   **b** 6kg 4g [   ]   **c** 5kg 70g [   ]

---

2 Record the answers to these questions in kilograms and grams.

a 18kg 690g ÷ 6 = [   ]   **c** 6kg 835g × 11 = [   ]

b 9kg – 7684g = [   ]   **d** 9.399kg + 0.9kg = [   ]

---

3 The contents of a box have a mass of 1 kg 680g.
Write in grams the following fractional amounts of this.

a $\frac{1}{3}$ [   ]   **c** $\frac{1}{4}$ [   ]   **e** $\frac{5}{6}$ [   ]

b $\frac{2}{3}$ [   ]   **d** $\frac{3}{4}$ [   ]   **f** $\frac{3}{8}$ [   ]

I CAN'T TALK I'M IN A WORKBOOK

---

4 Connect one of the values in the list to its approximate equal in the circle.

a

| 8 grams |
| 18 grams |
| 28 grams |

(1 ounce)

b

| 0.45 kilograms |
| 0.55 kilograms |
| 0.65 kilograms |

(1 pound)

---

5 Solve these problems.

a A delivery van contains 176 parcels each with a mass of 1.12kg.
Give the total mass of the parcels in kilograms to one decimal place. [   ]

b The mass of honey in a jar when full is 454g. The jar has a mass of 0.114kg.
Find the total mass of eight full jars of honey in kilograms and grams. [   ]

c Subtract 4kg 326g from 10.94kg and record your answer in grams. [   ]

Measuring Problems

1 Solve these problems.

a How many $\frac{1}{6}$ litre glasses can be filled from a $2\frac{1}{2}$ litre jug?

b A can of lemonade holds 275 millilitres. Find in litres the contents of forty cans.

c Nine bottles each hold 750ml. By how many litres and millilitres is their total capacity less than 8.5 litres?

d When an oil tank is one sixth full it holds 652 litres. How many litres will it hold when half full?

e For how many days would a 720ml bottle of cough medicine last if three 8ml spoonfuls were taken three times a day?

2 Write the answers to these calculations in millilitres in the boxes below the questions.

a 0.55 litres × 8

b 4242ml ÷ 6

c 9 litres + 7ml

d 4.3 litres – 2050ml

e $\frac{1}{5}$ litre + $\frac{3}{10}$ litre

f 0.4 litre – 0.25 litre

a		b		c		d		e		f	

3 Here are the dimensions of 2 cuboids. Work out the volume of each in cubic centimetres.

a 3cm × 5.5cm × 20mm

b 0.04mm × 30mm × 6cm

4 Make up dimensions of your own for two more cuboid shapes. Give the volume for each one.

5 Connect one of the values in the list to its approximate equal in the circle.

a

1 litre
4.5 litres
$2\frac{1}{2}$ litres

1 gallon

b

250 millilitres
1 litre
0.5 litre

1 pint

Measuring Problems

Mutant piranha

---

1 Fill in the blank times on the chart in the same way as the other times shown.

a

Departure time	Journey time	Arrival time
9.45am		12.09pm
3.15pm	5h 13min	
	4h 41min	12.01pm

b

Departure time	Arrival time	Journey time
06:20	12:22	
	13:03	3h 15min
16:15		5h 35min

---

2 Use the completed charts from Question 1 to answer this question.

At what time is the earliest departure in the day? ☐ and the latest? ☐

---

3 Express these times using the 24-hour clock system.

a 75 minutes before 3.14am ☐

c 99 minutes after 19:28 ☐

b 87 minutes after 14:03 ☐

d 25 minutes before 1.11pm ☐

---

4 Solve these problems.

a An aeroplane flew 2598 kilometres in 3 hours. If it travelled at a constant speed how far would it have travelled in 2 hours? ☐

b A train leaves at 15:22 and arrives at its destination $3\frac{1}{4}$ hours later. What time is that? ☐

c Edward reached school at 08:44. Donna came 27 minutes later. At what time did she arrive? ☐

d A bus departs every 35 minutes starting at 7:30am. What time does the sixth bus leave? ☐

---

5 Work out the difference in minutes between the two times given.

a 9.57pm, 12.15am ☐   **c** 23:36, 00:50 ☐   **e** 10.22am, 12.07pm ☐

b 6.14pm, 7.28pm ☐   **d** 05:12, 06:14 ☐   **f** 4.19pm, 6.31pm ☐

Using Data

1 Transfer the information from Chart A to Chart B and then answer the questions.

Chart A — Vertical bar chart showing favourite flowers

Chart B — Horizontal bar chart showing favourite flowers

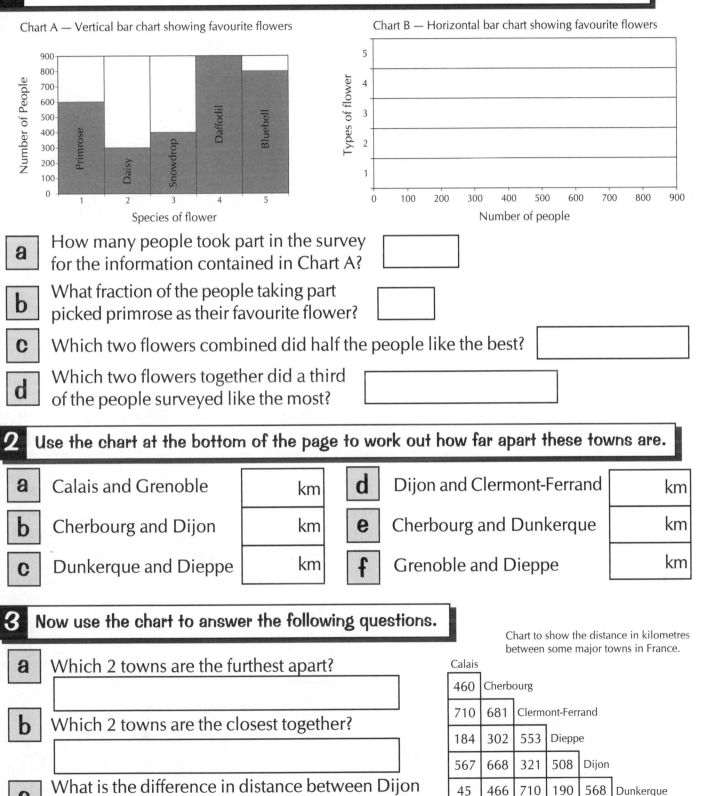

a How many people took part in the survey for the information contained in Chart A?

b What fraction of the people taking part picked primrose as their favourite flower?

c Which two flowers combined did half the people like the best?

d Which two flowers together did a third of the people surveyed like the most?

2 Use the chart at the bottom of the page to work out how far apart these towns are.

a Calais and Grenoble ___ km
b Cherbourg and Dijon ___ km
c Dunkerque and Dieppe ___ km
d Dijon and Clermont-Ferrand ___ km
e Cherbourg and Dunkerque ___ km
f Grenoble and Dieppe ___ km

3 Now use the chart to answer the following questions.

Chart to show the distance in kilometres between some major towns in France.

a Which 2 towns are the furthest apart?

b Which 2 towns are the closest together?

c What is the difference in distance between Dijon to Dieppe and Calais to Dunkerque? ___ km

Calais						
460	Cherbourg					
710	681	Clermont-Ferrand				
184	302	553	Dieppe			
567	668	321	508	Dijon		
45	466	710	190	568	Dunkerque	
861	923	295	763	298	862	Grenoble

33

Using Data

1 Look at the pie chart and then answer the questions about it.

a What fraction of the total waterfowl population on the lake were swans?

b Swans and mallard ducks make up what % of the waterfowl present on the lake?

c Which was the most common species of bird to be found there?

d What fraction of the waterfowl population was not made up of coot?

e What % of the waterfowl were not swans?

f What % of all the waterfowl were mallard ducks?

Waterfowl species shown as a proportion of the total number inhabiting Caterham Lake.

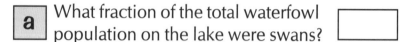

Swan

Other

72°

72°

Mallard 72°

144°

Coot

2 Read the information below. Display this information in different ways on the two bar graph axes at the bottom of the page. Remember to annotate your graphs correctly.

There are 30 children in Year 6 at Green Lane School. In a survey carried out by these children last July it was discovered that 10 of them walked to school, 12 came by car, 5 came by bus and the other 3 cycled.

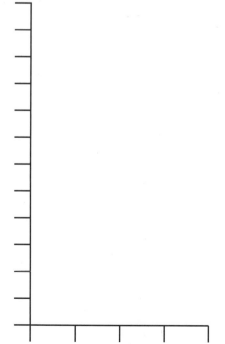

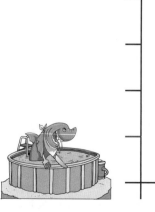

Using Data

1 Study the train timetable below and then use it to answer the questions.

Timetable for trains from Maxworthy to Pendleton   Mondays to Saturdays

Maxworthy	0504	0546	0709	0843	0956	1144	1230	1312	1436	1515	1652	1733	1927	2027	2157
Sheldon	0506	0548	0711	0845	0958	1146	1232	1314	1438	1517	1654	1735	1929	2029	2159
Thickwood	0509	0551	0714	0848	1001	1149	1235	1317	1441	1520	1657	1738	1932	2032	2202
Ashwell	0513	0555	0718	0852	1005	1153	1239	1321	1445	1524	1701	1742	1936	2036	2206
Antrobus	0517	0559	0722	0856	1009	1157	1243	1325	1449	1528	1705	1746	1940	2040	2210
Pendleton	0521	0603	0726	0900	1013	1201	1247	1329	1453	1532	1709	1750	1944	2044	2214

a How many trains a day leave Maxworthy for Pendleton?

b I'm at Thickwood station at 11.55am. Give the time of the next train to Pendleton.

c What is the difference in time between the departure of the first train from Maxworthy and the last?

d How many trains run from Thickwood to Antrobus after midday?

e The 11:46 train from Sheldon is delayed by 17 minutes. What time will it arrive in Pendleton?

f How long does it take to travel from Sheldon to Antrobus?

g I'm at Ashwell and want to reach Pendleton by 5.00pm. Which is the last train I can catch?

2 The speed-time graph shows a train journey lasting an hour.

a For how many minutes was the train travelling at 40mph?

b By how much did the train slow down between the fifteenth and twentieth minute of the trip?

c For approximately how long was the train stationary?

d What was the maximum speed attained by the train during the first 30 minutes?

e How much speed was gained between minutes 35 and 40?

Using Data

1 Connect each event to a suitable place on the chance line.

0   1

| You will get wet when you next have a bath. | You will see your classroom on a normal day at school. |

| You will spend Christmas Day on Mars. | You will get heads when you next toss a coin. |

2 Choose from the words below to answer these questions. What are the chances of...

certain   **very likely**   **likely**   **very unlikely**   **impossible**

a   being younger tomorrow than you are today?

b   wetting your hands when you submerge them in a bowl of water?

c   spending your next birthday on the summit of Mount Everest?

d   having something to eat when you next visit a cafe?

e   you seeing a train at a railway station?

3 A full pack of playing cards is placed face down on a desk. What is the chance of picking up...

a	a black card? 1:7, 1:3, 1:52, (1:2)	**g**	a black ace? 1:26, 1:3, 1:4, 1:8
b	a red king? 1:4, 1:26, 1:9, 1:7	**h**	an ace? 1:6, 1:9, 1:2, 1:13
c	a queen? 1:8, 1:2, 1:5, 1:13	**i**	a red jack? 1:8, 1:7, 1:4, 1:26
d	a diamond? 1:4, 1:15, 1:6, 1:2	**j**	a red card? 1:12, 1:8, 1:4, 1:2
e	ace of clubs? 1:3, 1:52, 1:9, 1:8	**k**	a five? 1:8, 1:13, 1:7, 1:5
f	a club? 1:4, 1:10, 1:3, 1:2	**l**	a spade? 1:4, 1:13, 1:9, 1:3

Shape, Symmetry & Movement

1 Name the shape hidden in each of these clues. Choose your answers from the word list.

a 2-D with 5 sides

b Parallelogram with all four sides equal

c 3-D with 6 square faces

d 3-D with 4 triangular faces

e 2-D with 6 sides

f Any 3-D shape with a number of faces

g 2-D with 4 sides and 4 right angles

h 3-D with 8 faces

i 3-D with a round base and a pointed top

j Round and 3-D

k 3-D polygon base with triangular sides rising to a point

l 2-D with 8 sides

polyhedron	pyramid	octahedron	pentagon	triangle	rhombus
square	cone	octagon	sphere	polygon	cylinder
cuboid	hexagon	rectangle	circle	tetrahedron	cube

a	b	c	d
e	f	g	h
i	j	k	l

2 This net shows a toy box without flaps.

a Work out the combined area of the top and bottom of the box in cm².

b How many end pieces of the box would be needed to cover the same area as the top of the box?

c How much less in cm² is the area of one of the sides than the area of the top?

d Give the total area of the net in cm².

e Calculate the volume of the completed box in cm³.

END · 6cm · 6cm

18cm · SIDE · BOTTOM · SIDE

END

TOP

9cm

Shape, Symmetry & Movement

1 Measure the approximate size of each angle and mark it on the drawing. Choose the correct angle name from the word list and write it in the box below each angle.

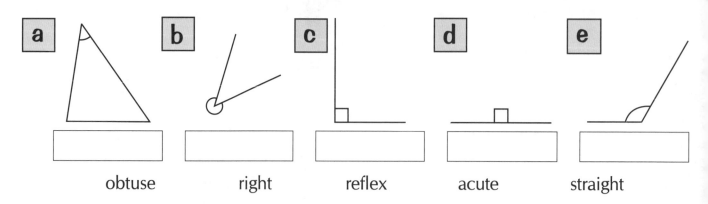

| **a** | **b** | **c** | **d** | **e** |

obtuse   right   reflex   acute   straight

2 Calculate the value of the missing angle in each group to make each set total a full turn.

a 113°, 86°, 142° | *19°* | **c** 164°, 44°, 38° | | **e** 53°, 163°, 32° | |

b 94°, 135°, 27° | | **d** 62°, 107°, 138° | | **f** 186°, 66°, 43° | |

3 Each question gives two of the internal angles of a triangle. Work out the third angle.

a 98°, 72° [ ]   **b** 56°, 91° [ ]   **c** 115°, 46° [ ]

4 In this diagram, which is not drawn to scale, the line AB is parallel to the line CD. Without using a protractor, work out the values of the angles a-e.

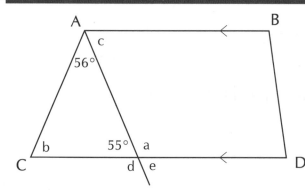

a = [   ]°

b = [   ]°

c = [   ]°

d = [   ]°

e = [   ]°

5 Work out how many degrees the minute hand of an analogue clock moves through in...

a 15 minutes [   ]   **b** half an hour [   ]   **c** 1½ hours [   ]

Shape, Symmetry & Movement

1 Write down the coordinates for each item shown on the grid in the box next to its name.

a	helicopter	
b	air balloon	
c	aeroplane	
d	bus	
e	space shuttle	
f	car	
g	boat	

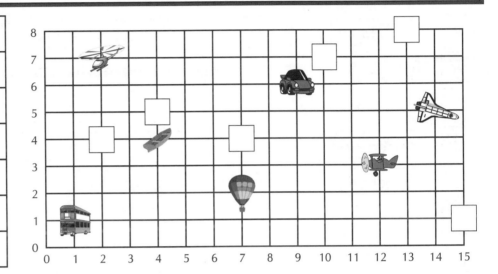

Write the letter shown next to each coordinate in the correct box on the grid.

| h | 4, 5 | A | j | 13, 8 | C | l | 10, 7 | E |
| i | 7, 4 | B | k | 15, 1 | D | m | 2, 4 | F |

2 Place a cross in the rectangle on the grid which is...

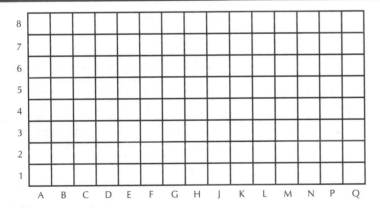

f	2 squares north of H1
g	4 squares above F1
h	7 squares to the right of C4
i	4 squares east of D5
j	3 squares south-east of A7
k	6 squares west of P6
l	5 squares north-west of Q1
m	5 squares to the left of J5
n	4 squares north-west of L1
o	1 square south of H8
p	1 square south-west of E7

a	2 squares north-east of F2
b	5 squares below K8
c	3 squares south of D6
d	11 squares to the left of Q7
e	3 squares south-west of H8

Shape, Symmetry & Movement

1 Join each word to its definition.

a	horizontal	being the same distance apart all the time — a
b	diagonal	the direction in which the hands of a clock move — b
c	column	flat and level with the horizon — c
d	clockwise	instrument for measuring angles — d
e	direction	crossing from one corner to the opposite corner — e
f	parallel	vertical line of numbers — f
g	angle	upright and perpendicular to the horizon — g
h	protractor	horizontal line of numbers — h
i	row	the line or course along which anything moves — i
j	vertical	the amount of turn between 2 lines where they meet — j

2 Write down a word to fit the meaning or a meaning to fit the word.

a	opposite	
b		the middle part of something
c	descend	
d		to go around and around
e	position	
f		a quarter of a circle
g	perpendicular	
h		beneath or below something
i	ascend	
j		a unit of measurement for angles

Answers — Pages 1 to 10

PAGE 1

Q1. a) (109), (118), 127, (136), 145, 154, (163), 172
 b) 362, 377, (392), 407, 422, 437, (452), (467)
 c) (215), 236, 257, (278), (299), 320, 341, 362
 d) −23, (−16), (−9), −2, 5, 12, (19), 26

Q2. These numbers should have triangles around them:
 45, 15, 21, 36

Q3. 1, 3, 6, 10, 28

Q4. a) four thousand and ninety
 b) three thousand eight hundred
 c) thirty-seven thousand and three
 d) five hundred and six thousand and forty

Q5. a) 3008 b) 30 409 c) 609 205

PAGE 2

Q1. a) 46 b) 8372 c) 521 d) 6900
 e) 3847 f) 1039

Q2. 2014 — less than twenty thousand
 20 001 — between twenty thousand and two hundred thousand
 200 659 — between two hundred thousand and one million
 4 846 392 — more than one million but less than ten million
 10 468 135 — more than ten million

Q3. a) 7951 b) 810 c) 451 d) 357

Q4. These numbers should have squares around them:
 25, 16, 49, 81

Q5. 1, 4, 9, 36, 64, 100, 121

PAGE 3

Q1. 1 and all multiples of 2,3,5 and 7 (except 2,3,5 and 7) should be shaded.
 2, 3, 5, 7, 11, 13, 17, 19, 23, 29, 31, 37, 41, 43, 47, 53, 59, 61, 67, 71, 73, 79, 83, 89, 97
 prime numbers

Q2. a) odd crossed out
 b) even crossed out
 c) odd crossed out

Q3. a) (4000 + 900 + 50 + 7)
 b) 6000 + 300 + 20 + 1
 c) 80 000 + 5000 + 600 + 3
 d) 70 000 + 2000 + 900 + 80 + 4

Q4. (360) − (341) − 322 − 303 − 284 − (265) − 246 − 227

Q5. 2500

PAGE 4

Q1. a) 306 b) 5089 c) 405 026
 d) 2 080 370 e) 30201

Q2. 123 456, 123 465, 123 645, 124 365, 124 653

Q3. 795 048, 789 504, 784 950, 780 945

Q4. 5

Q5. Accept amounts between the following numbers:
 a) 25 870 and 25 875, 25 875 or above
 b) below 55 109, 55 109 and 56 109
 c) above 10 000, below 9990
 d) above 60 606 60 606 and 56 109
 e) below 98 889, above 99 999

PAGE 5

Q1. a) 500, $^5/_{1000}$, 500 000, 5, 5 000 000
 b) 50 000, $^5/_{100}$, 50, 5000, $^5/_{10}$

Q2. - five million, four hundred and thirty-one thousand, six hundred and twenty
 - five hundred and seventy-six thousand, nine hundred and twenty-eight
 - three hundred and fifty-seven thousand and ninety-three
 - eighty-five thousand, four hundred and six
 - seventeen thousand, five hundred and eighty-three

Q3. a) = b) > c) > d) < e) = f) >

Q4. a) 87 654 310 b) 98 755 442

Q5. a) 33 445 679 b) 22 666 899

PAGE 6

Q1. a) 7562, 117 562
 b) 50 491, 160 491
 c) 316 485, 426 485
 d) 393 029, 503 029

Q2. a) 25 900 b) 30 300 c) 27 000
 d) 325 935 e) 485 400
 f) 610 250

Q3. −107, −104, −101, −99, 98, 100, 103, 106

Q4. 0.99, $^5/_8$, 0.75, $^3/_5$, 0.5, $^4/_{10}$, $^1/_3$, 0.25, 0.2, $^1/_6$, $^1/_{12}$

Q5. a) 5 b) 3.649

PAGE 7

Q1. a) 100 b) 1 000 000 c) 100 d) 10

Q2. 35 321 - 18 200, 7510 - 3700
 4958 - 2500, 49 612 - 24 000
 42 106 - 21 000, 31 658 - 15 600
 7510 + 4958 = roughly 12 500

Q3. a) 26 b) 148 c) 200 d) 101

Q4. a) 35.8 b) 174.4 c) 461.6 d) 95.2

Q5. a) 61 - 60 circled b) 38 + 53 circled

PAGE 8

Q1. a) 24 300 b) 36 900 c) 72 100

Q2. a) 3.9, 4 b) 22.5, 23 c) 7581, 7600
 d) 5765, 5800 e) 0.075, 0.08
 f) 0.505, ½

Q3. a) 500 b) 750 c) 2300 d) 1400
 e) 2250 f) 1200

Q4. a) 22 000, 26 000, 28 000
 b) −20, −10, 20, 40

Q5. a) 57 b) 78 c) 91 d) 26 e) 65

PAGE 9

Q1. a) 604 000 b) 396 000 c) 186 000
 d) 519 000 e) 427 000 f) 274 000

Q2. The following values should be circled:
 a) 0.04, $^3/_{100}$ b) 71%, $^7/_{10}$
 c) $^3/_9$, 33% d) $^3/_4$, 74%
 e) $^7/_{16}$, $^3/_8$ f) $^1/_2$, 0.49

Q3. a) 0.3, 0.5, 0.6, 0.8
 b) 0.02, 0.04, 0.07, 0.09

Q4. a) 1000 b) 2500 c) 3000 d) 1500
 e) 4500 f) 2000

Q5. The following numbers should be circled:
 a) 34 251 b) 13 758 c) 66 750
 d) 55 780

PAGE 10

Q1. 10 boxes should be coloured red and 1 box coloured green.

Q2. a) $^{19}/_3$ b) $^{57}/_8$ c) $^{35}/_6$ d) $^{115}/_{12}$ e) $^{33}/_4$
 f) $^{101}/_{12}$ g) $^{77}/_8$ h) $^{53}/_{12}$

Q3. a) 90 b) 2, 4, 7, 3 c) 60 min

Q4. a) 16 b) 64 c) 37 d) 80 e) 11
 f) 45 g) 5 h) 78 i) 12 j) 29

Q5. a) (40 + 5 + $^8/_{10}$ + $^6/_{100}$)
 b) 600 + 80 + $^1/_{10}$
 c) 50 + 2 + $^3/_{100}$ + $^6/_{1000}$
 d) $^4/_{100}$ + $^5/_{1000}$
 e) 6 + $^3/_{10}$ + $^2/_{100}$ + $^5/_{1000}$
 f) $^8/_{10}$ + $^4/_{100}$ + $^6/_{1000}$

Answers — Pages 11 to 20

PAGE 11

Q1. a) $^{11}/_{12}$ b) $^2/_3$ c) $^5/_{12}$ d) $^5/_8$ e) $^7/_8$
f) $1^1/_4$ g) $^7/_8$ h) $^5/_6$

Q2. 4 boxes should be coloured blue and 5 boxes coloured yellow.

Q3. a) $6^5/_9$ b) $5^3/_5$ c) $5^3/_7$ d) $3^5/_8$ e) $3^4/_5$
f) $10^1/_3$ g) $22^1/_2$ h) $5^3/_{10}$ i) $3^4/_7$
j) $8^2/_5$

Q4. a) $(3 + 0.4 + 0.07, 3^{47}/_{100}$,
$3 + ^4/_{10} + ^7/_{100})$
b) $10 + 5 + 0.9 + 0.03, 15^{93}/_{100}$,
$10 + 5 + ^9/_{10} + ^3/_{100}$
c) $20 + 1 + 0.6 + 0.007, 21^{607}/_{1000}$,
$20 + 1 + ^6/_{10} + ^7/_{1000}$

Q5. a) 80 b) 60 c) 70 d) 180 e) 28
f) 42 g) 34 h) 43 i) 90 j) 106

PAGE 12

Q1. a) 103.17 b) 10.22 c) 2.264
d) 77.85 e) 3.916 f) 6.963
g) 279.53 h) 94.46 i) 86.85

Q2. a) $^4/_5$ b) $^2/_5$ c) $^{11}/_{20}$ d) $^3/_4$ e) $^1/_{10}$
f) $^3/_{20}$ g) $^{19}/_{20}$ h) $^1/_4$ i) $^1/_2$ j) $^3/_{10}$

Q3. a) $^1/_2$ b) $^1/_{12}$ c) $^1/_{12}$ d) $^1/_{12}$ e) $^1/_6$
f) $^5/_{12}$ g) $^1/_8$ h) $^1/_6$

Q4. a) 3101 b) 3015 c) 1456 d) 3990
e) 7824 f) 922 g) 726 h) 5210
i) 4025 j) 1248 k) 4554 l) 854

Q5. a) 0.25 b) 0.15 c) 0.07 d) 0.4
e) 0.37 f) 0.01 g) 0.75 h) 0.65
i) 0.3 j) 0.43

PAGE 13

Q1. Many combinations – each number must be 2-digit.

Q2. a) 3486 b) 2571 c) 9245 d) 1434

Q3. 6425 + 2565 = 8990
4479 + 2145 = 6624
3163 + 3979 = 7142
1279 + 5275 = 6554
3218 + 3319 = 6537

Q4. a) 10 550 b) 12 840 c) 12 290

Q5. a) 43 608 b) 38 730 c) 48 152
d) 37 026 e) 45 492 f) 35 078
g) 31 384 h) 28 568 i) 56 150

PAGE 14

Q1. a) 980 b) 740 c) 955 d) 1410
e) 7200 f) 565 g) 1010 h) 870
i) 670

Q2. a) 3175, (3025)
3375, 3225
(3575), 3425
b) (2665), 2815
2845, 2995
3005, (3155)

Q3. a) 5 b) 5 c) 7

Q4. a) Completed example.
b) 2045, (625), (2670)
(745), 3365, (4110)
2790, (3990), 6780
c) (680), (4095), 4775
780, (425), (1205)
(1460), 4520, 5980

Q5. a) 6725 b) 6831 c) 8432

PAGE 15

Q1. a) 7940 b) 9946 c) 8432 d) 9430
e) 15 450

Q2. a) (2080, 4160) b) 3260, 6520
c) 4940, 9880 d) 3160, 6320
e) 4300, 8600 f) 2780, 5560
g) 4540, 9080 h) 2560, 5120
i) 4320, 8640

Q3. Open ended – ten addition sums each with three numbers and using all the numbers from the central grid.

Q4. a) two thousand, nine hundred and thirty-one
b) six thousand, nine hundred and seventy-three

Q5. a) 9082 b) 5309

PAGE 16

Q1. a) 7180 b) 5880 c) 3190

Q2. 7090 – 1258 = 5832
9256 – 3809 = 5447
8600 – 3213 = 5387
7535 – 1177 = 6358
7625 – 1938 = 5687

Q3. Open ended but each answer must have a 2-digit number subtracted from a 3-digit number.

Q4. a) (998 – 658 = 340)
b) 854 – 238 = 616
or 854 – 616 = 238
c) 423 – 213 = 210
or 423 – 210 = 213
d) 407 – 226 = 181
or 407 – 181 = 226
e) 940 – 817 = 123
or 940 – 123 = 817
f) 700 – 319 = 381
or 700 – 381 = 319

Q5. a) 338 b) 477 c) 613 d) 1314

PAGE 17

Q1. 362 – 700 / 338, (289 – 600 / 311)
413 – 900 / 487, 225 – 400 / 175
305 – 500 / 195

Q2. a) 875 b) 1010 c) 550 d) 750 e) 1250
f) 875 g) 325 h) 1450 i) 425

Q3. a) 3220 b) 3549

Q4. a) 837, (1738)
155, 1056
(319), 1220
b) (11 874), 14 500
10 405, 13 031
7737, (10 363)

Q5. a) 4577 b) 2382 c) 4596

PAGE 18

Q1. a) 269 b) 5564 c) 2272 d) 2479
e) 4965

Q2. Many combinations – a different number from the grid should be chosen for each sum and the answer worked out correctly.

Q3. a) 1356 b) 3430 c) 4694 d) 7126
e) 7907 f) 3875 g) 5783 h) 2018

Q4. a) three thousand, five hundred and fifteen
b) two thousand, eight hundred and twenty

Q5. a) 6911 b) 12 793

PAGE 19

Q1. a) 81 b) 1600 c) 400 d) 144
e) 100 f) 3600 g) 2500 h) 900
i) 6400 j) 4900 k) 8100 l) 10 000

Q2. a) 180 b) 210 c) 270 d) 375 e) 495

Q3. a) Eighty-two thousand, four hundred and seventy
b) Fifty-five thousand, nine hundred and fifty-three
c) Ninety-six thousand and twenty-four

Q4. $7 \times 657 = 4599$, $701 \times 6 = 4206$,
$5 \times 890 = 4450$, $591 \times 8 = 4728$,
$523 \times 9 = 4707$

Q5. a) 1992 b) 900 c) 11 880 d) 8064

PAGE 20

Q1. These numbers should be circled:
90, 1440, 468, 423, 1080, 189, 1170, 540, 1530, 378

Q2. a) 180 b) 15 c) 60 d) 125 e) 50
f) 80 g) 630 h) 40 i) 90

Q3. a) 12 584 b) 51 936 c) 25 680
d) 71 664 e) 43 088

Q4. a) 13 394 b) 7002 c) 14 850
d) 9328 e) 23 569 f) 7038

Q5. a) (1100), 2200
2200, 4400
4400, (8800)
b) 1350, (2700)
2700, 5400
(5400), 10 800

Answers — Pages 21 to 30

PAGE 21

Q1. a) 32 656 b) 43 088 c) 22 092
d) 62 415 e) 57 876

Q2. a) 167 220 b) 13 887 c) 9493
d) 4535

Q3. a) Many answers – six multiples of 8 which are greater than 200.
b) Many answers – six multiples of both 4 and 6 which are greater than 100.

Q4. (102 – 2040), 137 – 2740,
146 – 2920, 120 – 2400,
109 – 2180, 115 – 2300,
154 – 3080, 128 – 2560,
143 – 2860

Q5. a) 173 880 b) 90 720

PAGE 22

Q1. a) 51 b) 65 c) 73 d) 30 e) 104
f) 109 g) 54 h) 81 i) 19 j) 106

Q2. a) six hundred and fifty-one
b) one thousand, one hundred and fifty-seven
c) one thousand, three hundred and ninety
d) one thousand and twenty-eight

Q3. $5125 \div 5 = 1025$
$9486 \div 9 = 1054$
$6468 \div 6 = 1078$
$8520 \div 8 = 1065$
$7854 \div 7 = 1122$

Q4. a) 96 b) 2084
c) Open ended – any 2 numbers with a quotient of 15.

Q5. a) 182 r 2 b) 140 r 2 c) 93 r 5

PAGE 23

Q1. a) 50 b) 500 c) 7 d) 80 e) 490
f) 6 g) 60 h) 640 i) 60

Q2. a) 1030 b) 1044 c) 337 d) 408
e) 1197

Q3. a) (140), 624
70, 312
35, (156)
b) 1976, (796)
988, 398
(494), 199

Q4. a) 1 / 144, 2 / 72, 3 / 48, 4 / 36,
6 / 24, 8 / 18, 9 / 16, 12 / 12
b) 1 / 168, 2 / 84, 3 / 56, 4 / 42,
6 / 28, 7 / 24, 8 / 21, 12 / 14
c) 1 / 180, 2 / 90, 3 / 60, 4 / 45,
5 / 36, 9 / 20, 10 / 18, 12 / 15

Q5. a) fifteen b) seventeen

PAGE 24

Q1. a) 827 b) 923 c) 797 d) 710 r 1
e) 1340 r 1 f) 206 r 3 g) 664
h) 1038 r 2

Q2. a) $(772 \div 4 = 193)$
b) $305 \div 5 = 61$ or $305 \div 61 = 5$
c) $876 \div 6 = 146$ or $876 \div 146 = 6$
d) $595 \div 7 = 85$ or $595 \div 85 = 7$
e) $776 \div 8 = 97$ or $776 \div 97 = 8$
f) $171 \div 9 = 19$ or $171 \div 19 = 9$

Q3. a) 635 b) 26

Q4. The following calculations should be circled:
a) $5000 \div 8$ b) $2856 \div 7$
c) $1281 \div 7$ d) $2439 \div 9$
e) $9063 \div 9$ f) $6300 \div 9$

Q5. a) 378 b) 149

PAGE 25

Q1. a) £5.27 b) £13.28 c) $\frac{1}{6}$
d) £13.00 e) 70p

Q2. a) £54.32 b) £98.40 c) £70.26

Q3. a) 46p b) £1.56 c) £2.20

Q4. a) £99.03 b) £85.66 c) £18.71

Q5. a) £15.00 b) 50p c) £2.25
d) £4.20

PAGE 26

Q1. a) £5.25 b) £7.35 c) £1.05

Q2. £7.34, (£10.66), £12.91, £14.12,
£8.45, £11.80, £13.58, (£9.23),
£15.77

Q3. 675p, 222p, (618p), 997p, 803p,
450p, (911p), 376p, 284p

Q4. a) £43.14 b) £3.63 c) £139.20

Q5. a) (29p, 58%) b) 17p, 34%
c) 35p, 70% d) 24p, 48%
e) 41p, 82% f) 43p, 86%

PAGE 27

Q1. a) £4.14 b) £1.17 c) £5.67
d) £13.86
12%

Q2. a) (£41.58, £124.74)
£70.30, £210.90
£32.62, £97.86
b) £102.04, £306.12
£96.94, £290.82
£135.28, £405.84
c) £189.06, £567.18
£145.60, £436.80
£166.52, £499.56

Q3. a) (£91 875.00, £18 375.00
£3675.00, £735.00)
b) £7812.50, £1562.50
£312.50, £62.50
c) £862.50, £172.50
£34.50, £6.90

Q4. £14.60, fourteen pounds sixty pence

Q5. £9.36

PAGE 28

Q1. 60

Q2. £4.58, four pounds fifty-eight pence.

Q3. a) £25.58 b) £9.50 c) Desk diary
d) 52p, £4.68 e) 20, 19p

Q4. £15.84

Q5. two pounds forty pence

PAGE 29

Q1. A = 1050 mm²
B = 450 mm²
C = 250 mm²
D = 750 mm²

Q2. 12.5 cm² (12 ½ cm²)
40 cm

Q3. a) 768 cm² b) 298 m c) 378 m²

Q4. a) 31 cm b) 74 cm c) 83 cm
d) 65 cm e) 42 cm f) 57 cm

Q5. a) 4500 m b) 15 250 m c) 27 025 m

PAGE 30

Q1. a) 3207g b) 6004g c) 5070g

Q2. a) 3kg 115g b) 1kg 316g
c) 75kg 185g d) 10kg 299g

Q3. a) 560g b) 1120g c) 420g
d) 1260g e) 1400g f) 630g

Q4. a) 28g — 1 ounce
b) 0.45kg — 1 pound

Q5. a) 197.1 kg b) 4kg 544g c) 6614g

Answers — Pages 31 to 40

PAGE 31

Q1. a) 15 b) 11 litres c) 1 litre 750ml
d) 1956 litres e) 10 days

Q2. a) 4400ml b) 707ml c) 9007ml
d) 2250ml e) 500ml f) 150ml

Q3. a) 33 cm³   b) 72 cm³

Q4. Open ended – 2 sets of cuboid
dimensions with volumes for each set.

Q5. a) 4.5 litres – 1 gallon
b) 0.5 litres – 1 pint

PAGE 32

Q1. a) 2 h 24 min
8.28 pm
7.20 am
b) 6 h 2 min
09:50
21:50

Q2. 06:20, 16:15

Q3. a) 01:59 b) 15:30 c) 21:07
d) 12:46

Q4. a) 1732 km b) 18:37 c) 09:11
d) 10.25 am

Q5. Answers in minutes:
a) 138 b) 74 c) 74 d) 62 e) 105
f) 132

PAGE 33

Q1. Information from Chart A should be
displayed horizontally on Chart B
a) 3000   b) ¹/₅
c) Primrose and daffodil
d) Primrose and snowdrop

Q2. a) 861 km   b) 668 km   c) 190 km
d) 321 km   e) 466 km   e) 763 km

Q3. a) Cherbourg and Grenoble
b) Calais and Dunkerque
c) 463 km

PAGE 34

Q1. a) ¹/₅ b) 40% c) Coot d) ³/₅
e) 80% f) 20%

Q2.

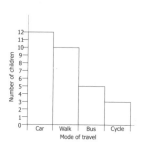

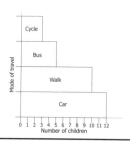

PAGE 35

Q1. a) 15 b) 12:35 c) 16h 53min d) 9
e) 12:18 f) 11 minutes g) 15:24

Q2. a) 15 min
b) 20mph
c) Accept any value between 2 and 3
minutes.
d) 60mph
e) 40mph

PAGE 36

Q1.

Q2. a) impossible   b) certain
c) very unlikely   d) very likely
e) likely

Q3. a) 1:2 b) 1:26 c) 1:13 d) 1:4
e) 1:52 f) 1:4 g) 1:26 h) 1:13
i) 1:26 j) 1:2 k) 1:13 l) 1:4

PAGE 37

Q1. a) pentagon   b) rhombus
c) cube   d) tetrahedron
e) hexagon   f) polyhedron
g) rectangle   h) octahedron
i) cone   j) sphere
k) pyramid   l) octagon

Q2. a) 324cm² b) 3 c) 54cm²
d) 648cm² e) 972cm³

PAGE 38

Q1. a) accept any answer between 44° and
48° inclusive, acute
b) accept any answer between 305°
and 315° inclusive, reflex
c) 90°, right
d) 180°, straight
e) accept any answer between 118° and
122° inclusive, obtuse

Q2. a) (19°) b) 104° c) 114° d) 53°
e) 112° f) 65°

Q3. a) 10° b) 33° c) 19°

Q4. a = 125°, b = 69°, c = 55°,
d = 125°, e = 55°

Q5. a) 90° b) 180° c) 540°

PAGE 39

Q1. a) 2, 7 b) 7, 2 c) 12, 3 d) 1, 1
e) 14, 5 f) 9, 6 g) 4,4
h) - onwards
- check that the position of each
letter on the grid is correct.

Q2. Check that the position of each cross on
the grid is correct - they should form the
word 'Hi'.

PAGE 40

Q1. a) a - c b) b - e c) c - f d) d - b
e) e - i f) f - a g) g - j h) h - d
i) i - h j) j - g

Q2. a) in a position face to face
b) centre
c) to come or go down
d) rotate
e) the place taken by somebody or
something
f) quadrant
g) at right angles to the horizontal
h) underneath
i) to come or go up
j) degree